Level 3

Guided Practice Book

Building
VOCABULARY
from Word Roots

prehistoric

biplane

explosion

Authors

Timothy Rasinski, Nancy Padak, Rick M. Newton, and Evangeline Newton

Teacher Created Materials

Credits

Editor
Christine Dugan, M.A. Ed.

Assistant Editor
Leslie Huber, M.A.

Senior Editor
Lori Kamola, M.S. Ed.

Editor-in-Chief
Sharon Coan, M.S. Ed.

Editorial Manager
Gisela Lee, M.A.

Creative Director
Lee Aucoin

Cover Design
Lee Aucoin

Imaging
Deb Brown
Robin Erickson
Don Tran
Phil Garcia

ELL Consultants
Melina E. Castillo, Ed.D.
Bilingual Curriculum Supervisor
Division of Bilingual Education
and World Languages
Miami-Dade County Public Schools

Carmen Zuñiga Dunlap, Ph.D.
Associate Dean, College of Education
California State University, Fullerton

Karie A. Feldner, M.S. Ed.

Maria Elvira Gallardo, M.A.

Publisher
Rachelle Cracchiolo, M.S.Ed.

To order additional copies of this book or any other Teacher Created Materials products, go to www.tcmpub.com or call 1-800-858-7339.

Teacher Created Materials

5301 Oceanus Drive
Huntington Beach, CA 92649-1030
www.tcmpub.com
ISBN 978-0-7439-0653-1
© 2007 Teacher Created Materials
Reprinted 2009
Made in U.S.A.

Part A:
Meet the Root

Divide and Conquer

Directions: "Divide" two-syllable compound words into two words. Then "conquer" them by writing the meaning of the compound words.

	base word	base word	compound word means
	bed	room	room for a bed
1. bedroom	_____	_____	_____
2. footprint	_____	_____	_____
3. mailbox	_____	_____	_____
4. backpack	_____	_____	_____
5. sidewalk	_____	_____	_____
6. shoelace	_____	_____	_____
7. carsick	_____	_____	_____
8. skateboard	_____	_____	_____
9. tiptoe	_____	_____	_____
10. sailboat	_____	_____	_____

Part B:
Combine and Create

Solving Riddles

Directions: Here are some riddles. The answers are compound words.

I am a box. Mail gets put in me.

I am a _____ .

I am an animal. I swim in water. My color is gold.

I am a _____ .

My second part means a trim. My first part is on your head.

I am a _____ .

I am a machine. I fly in the sky.

I am an _____ .

I am flat. You can stand on me. I let you skate.

I am a _____ .

Part C:
Read and Reason

Advice Column

Directions: Read the following advice column and follow Adelia Advice's suggestion to think of some other compound words you might already know.

Dear Adelia Advice,

At school, I am having some trouble understanding compound words. What are they?

Your Friend,
Confused Compound

Dear Confused Compound,
Have you ever woken up to a beautiful morning and felt the sun's light hit your face? (sunlight) Have you ever walked along the beach making prints with your bare feet? (footprints) Have you ever seen a fish that is gold? (goldfish) Do you carry your school books in a pack strapped to your back? (backpack)

Compound words are two words put together to make one word. Most often, they seem to fit together, like the suggestions above.

Your Friend,
Adelia Advice

Can you list compound words you might already know?

_____   _____

_____   _____

_____   _____

Part D:
Extend and Explore

Making Compound Words

Directions: Combine the words at the bottom of the page to make compound words that mean the following:

1. A place for recreation _____

2. Below the earth _____ *ground* _____

3. A friend to have fun with ___ *play* _____

4. Someone on the same side as you_____

5. Someone you learn with _____ *class* _____

6. A place in a school _____ *room* _____

7. Someone you live with_____ *under* _____

8. A place to sleep _____ *bed room* _____

Words

bed   class   ground   mate   play   room   team   under

Part E:
Go for the Gold!

Nine Square Wordo

Directions: This game is like Bingo. First, choose a free box and mark it with an X. Then choose eight of the twelve words from the word list provided by your teacher and write one word in each box. You can choose the box for each word. Then, your teacher will give a clue for each word. Make an X in the box for each word you match to the clue. If you get three words in a row, column, or diagonal, call out, "Wordo!"

Divide and Conquer

Directions: "Divide" three-syllable compound words into two words. Then "conquer" them by writing the meaning of the compound words.

	base word	base word	compound word means
1. honeybee	honey	bee	bee that makes honey
2. loudspeaker			
3. lawnmower			
4. trailblazer			
5. fingernail			
6. lowercase			
7. uppercase			
8. waterfall			
9. scorekeeper			
10. watercolors			

Part B:
Combine and Create

Making and Writing Words

Directions: Look at the clues. Write a word that fits the clue. You can only use the vowels and consonants listed. The special word uses all the letters.

Consonants: b, d, h, r, s   Vowels: e, i, o, u

1. Its bed is a nest. (four letters) ___ ___ ___ ___

2. Where we sleep at night (three letters) ___ ___ ___

3. Add one letter to #1 to make more than one bird. ___ ___ ___ ___ ___

4. A small building used to store things (four letters) ___ ___ ___ ___

5. A larger building where people live (five letters) ___ ___ ___ ___ ___

Special Word: the #5 for a #1

___ ___ ___ ___ ___ ___ ___ ___

A Compound Poem

Directions: Read the poem and find all the compound words.

> Some words go together
> In any kind of weather.
> Animals have compounds
> That are sometimes nouns.
> Bees live in a hive—beehive.
> Birds can live in a house—birdhouse.
> Honey comes from bees—honeybees.
> Honey can come on a comb—honeycomb.
> Some words go together
> In any kind of weather.

_____

_____

_____

_____

Part D:

Extend and Explore

Word Skits

Directions: With one or more partners, choose a word from "Divide and Conquer" on page 9.

Write the word and its definition on an index card.

Work together to create a skit to show the meaning of the word—without talking!

Show your skit to others. See if they can guess your word.

Part E:
Go for the Gold!

Nine Square Wordo

Directions: This game is like Bingo. First, choose a free box and mark it with an X. Then choose eight of the twelve words from the word list provided by your teacher and write one word in each box. You can choose the box for each word. Then, your teacher will give a clue for each word. Make an X in the box for each word you match to the clue. If you get three words in a row, column, or diagonal, call out, "Wordo!"

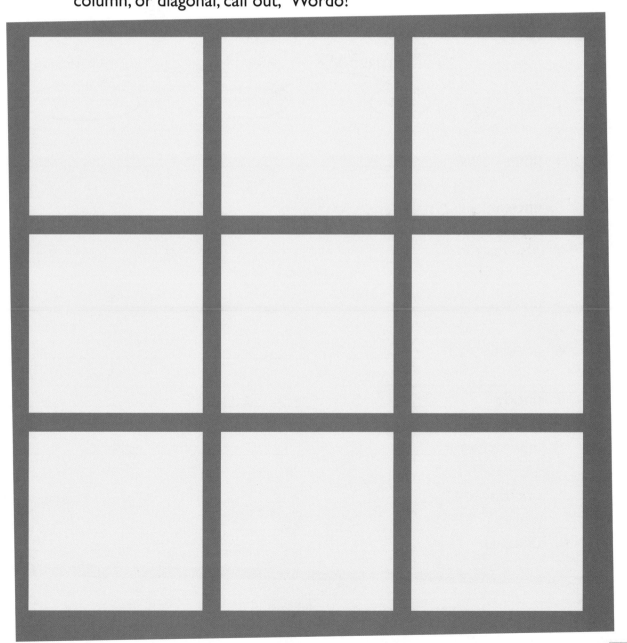

Part A:
Meet the Root

Divide and Conquer

Directions: Divide and conquer the words.
Remember, *un-* means "not."

	prefix means	base is	word means
1. unpacked	not	packed	not packed
2. unbuttoned			
3. unclean			
4. unlocked			
5. unhappy			
6. unable			
7. untidy			
8. unwrapped			
9. unchanged			
10. unequal			

Part B:
Combine and Create

Add a Prefix

Directions: The prefix *un-* can be added to one word in each sentence. Find the word. Write it with the prefix *un-*. Then rewrite the sentence with the new *un-* word so that it makes sense.

1. Rick is able to walk one mile.

   Un+ :_____

   New sentence: _____

2. She had to fold the sheets to put them on the shelf.

   Un+ :_____

   New sentence: _____

3. We locked the door when we left the house.

   Un+:_____

   New sentence: _____

4. I wrapped the new puppy with a blanket so he could sleep.

   Un+ :_____

   New sentence: _____

Part C:
Read and Reason

Short Story

Directions: Read the short story below, and then answer the questions that follow.

Our basketball team last year was pretty good! After nine games, we were unbeaten and untied. We were unbeatable—until our last game. That's when our season unraveled. Everything came unglued. We were behind by one point with just ten seconds left. Our star player had the ball and was heading for an easy slam dunk. But his shoe laces were untied. He tripped and fell. Needless to say, he was unable to make that basket that we needed so badly. We finally lost a game. It was such an unusual event that we didn't know how to act. Some of us cried. Others were stunned. Even our fans felt uneasy about our loss. Although we were unhappy, we all knew we had an unbelievable season—one that we would never forget.

1. What was the team's final record? _____

2. In this story, what do *unraveled* and *unglued* mean?_____

   _____

3. Have you ever felt uneasy about something? Describe a time when

   you felt uneasy._____

   _____

4. Think of an *un-* word that means the same as "one that we would

   never forget." _____

Part D:
Extend and Explore

"Timed" Word Trees

Directions: Work with a partner to fill the tree with *un-* words. You and your partner are a team. The team that brainstorms the most words and definitions will win!

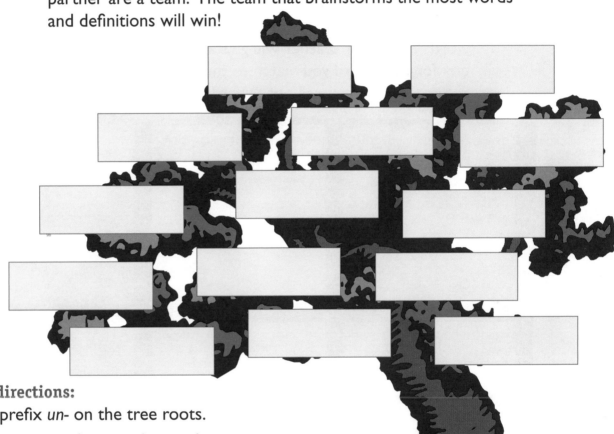

Follow these directions:

1. Write the prefix *un-* on the tree roots.

2. Write the meaning of *un-* on the trunk.

3. Write as many *un-* words on each branch as you can in two minutes.

4. Trade papers with your partner.

5. On a separate sheet of paper, write the meaning of your partner's *un-* words. Write as many as you can in two minutes.

6. How many different words and definitions did your team come up with? (If the same word is on both of your trees, count it only once!)

Part E:
Go for the Gold!

Nine Square Wordo

Directions: This game is like Bingo. First, choose a free box and mark it with an X. Then choose eight of the twelve words from the word list provided by your teacher and write one word in each box. You can choose the box for each word. Then, your teacher will give a clue for each word. Make an X in the box for each word you match to the clue. If you get three words in a row, column, or diagonal, call out, "Wordo!"

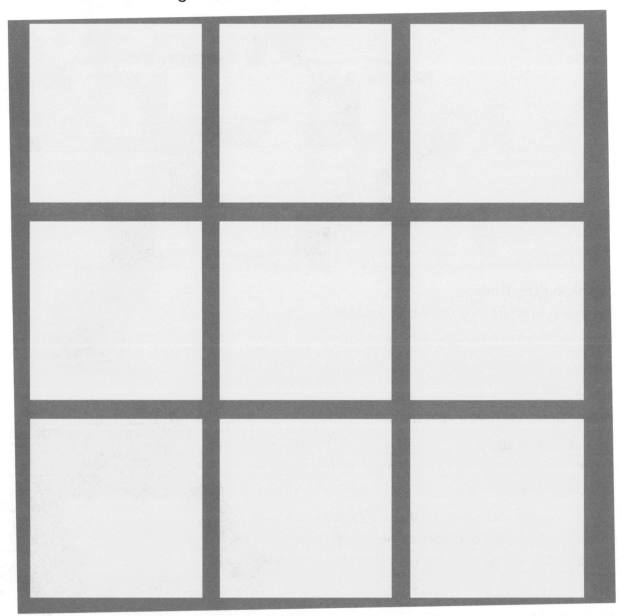

Part A:
Meet the Root

Divide and Conquer

Directions: "Divide" words into prefixes and base words.
Then "conquer" them by writing the meaning of the words.

		prefix means	base is	word means
1.	repay	back	pay	pay back
2.	reenter			
3.	reread			
4.	remake			
5.	rebuild			
6.	recount			
7.	recharge			
8.	refill			
9.	rewrite			
10.	restate			

Part B:
Combine and Create

Prefix Clues

Directions: Work with a partner. Make words that start with
re- and that have the given letter as the third letter. Make sure
the words have something to do with "again."

1. C: re + _____ = _____

2. F: re + _____ = _____

3. P: re + _____ = _____

4. S: re + _____ = _____

Directions: Use the words from numbers one through four above. Tell what
the words mean. Be sure to use "again."

5. The word is _____. It means _____ .

6. The word is _____. It means _____ .

7. The word is _____. It means _____ .

8. The word is _____. It means _____ .

Directions: Fill in the blanks with words that start with *re-*.

9. My sister's block tower fell down, so she had to _____ it.

10. I lost my homework, so I had to _____ it.

11. We have so many plants that we need to _____
the watering can three times.

12. I lost track of how many baseball cards I have, so now I need to

_____ them.

Part C:
Read and Reason

Poem

Directions: Read this short poem about the *re-* prefix several times until you think you can read it with good phrasing and expression.

Re- is a prefix that I love to see,
Because it means to do things repeatedly.
I rebuild my fort when it falls down.
I return to the circus each year for the clowns.
I reread my book before taking a test,
And reruns on TV are often the best.
So if you want to do something again and again,
Re- is the prefix for you, my friend!

Draw a picture of something you always like to "redo."

Write a sentence that tells why you like to do it "again and again"!

_____

Part D:
Extend and Explore

Word Reconstruct

Directions: Read the clues. Write each new word.

P	A	I	R

1. Add two letters (word means "to fix")

2. Change two letters (word means "to stay")

3. Subtract two letters (word means "what comes in a storm")

4. Add one letter (word means "to get into shape")

5. Add two letters (word means "to get yourself ready for another skill")

6. Subtract one letter (word means "to keep or hold back")

7. Subtract three letters (word means "to have run")

Part E:
Go for the Gold!

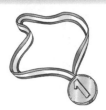

Nine Square Wordo

Directions: This game is like Bingo. First, choose a free box and mark it with an X. Then choose eight of the twelve words from the word list provided by your teacher and write one word in each box. You can choose the box for each word. Then, your teacher will give a clue for each word. Make an X in the box for each word you match to the clue. If you get three words in a row, column, or diagonal, call out, "Wordo!"

Part A:
Meet the Root

Divide and Conquer

Directions: "Divide" words into prefixes and base words. Then "conquer" them by writing the meaning of the words.

	prefix means	base is	word means
1. preheat	before	heat	heat before
2. predict			
3. premixed			
4. preshrunk			
5. presoak			
6. prejudge			
7. precook			
8. prefix			
9. prewashed			
10. prepay			

Part B:
Combine and Create

Odd Word Out

Directions: Look at the four words. Write the one that doesn't belong on the line. Then write how the other words are the same.

| precook | preheat | premixed | pretest |

1. The word that doesn't belong is _____ .

   The other words are the same because _____

   _____ .

| prehistoric | preshrink | presoak | prewash |

2. The word that doesn't belong is _____ .

   The other words are the same because _____

   _____ .

| premature | premed | premixed | prenatal |

3. The word that doesn't belong is _____ .

   The other words are the same because _____

   _____ .

Directions: *Pre-* means "before." Tell what these words mean. Be sure to use "before" in the definition.

4. Prehistoric means _____ .

5. Prepackage means _____ .

6. Preshrink means _____ .

7. Preview means _____ .

8. Prejudge means _____ .

Part C:
Read and Reason

Poem

Directions: Read the poem in the arrow. Can you write your own poem about *pre-* by using the words precook, pretest, and preview?

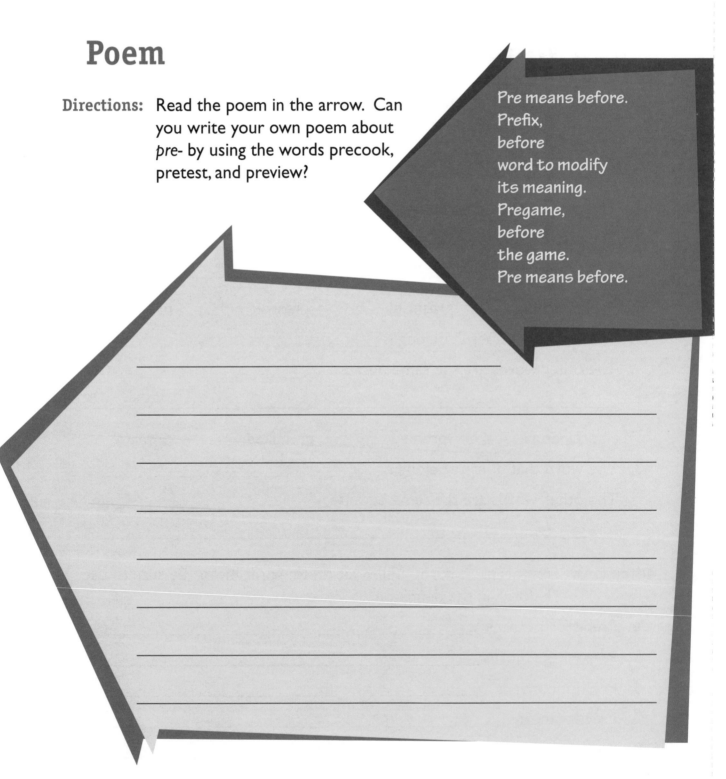

Pre means before.
Prefix,
before
word to modify
its meaning.
Pregame,
before
the game.
Pre means before.

Part D:
Extend and Explore

Word Invention Riddles

Directions: Work with a partner to invent new *un-*, *re-*, and *pre-* words. Follow these directions.

1.   Make up words using the prefixes *un-*, *re-*, and *pre-*.
2.   Choose one of your invented words to create a riddle.
3.   Write the invented word.
4.   Write three clues to help others figure it out.
5.   One of the clues must describe the meaning of the prefix.
6.   Choose one invented word riddle to share with the class. See if they can figure it out!

Here is an example:

Clues:

1. It is an animal that gallops.
2. It gallops before breakfast.
3. It has a long tail.

Invented Word: prehorse

Now you try it!

Clues:

1. _____

2. _____

3. _____

Invented Word: _____

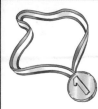

Part E:
Go for the Gold!

Nine Square Wordo

Directions: This game is like Bingo. First, choose a free box and mark it with an X.
Then choose eight of the twelve words from the word list provided by your
teacher and write one word in each box. You can choose the box for each
word. Then, your teacher will give a clue for each word. Make an X in the
box for each word you match to the clue. If you get three words in a row,
column, or diagonal, call out, "Wordo!"

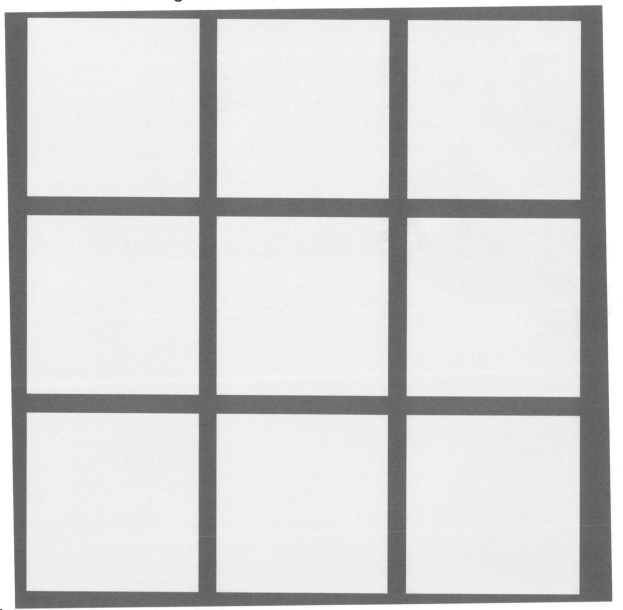

Part A:
Meet the Root

Divide and Conquer

Directions: Your teacher will give you a list of words. "Divide" words into word units (either as the two parts of a compound word or as a prefix and a base word). Then "conquer" them by writing the meaning of the words.

	word	word unit	word unit	word means
1.	_____	_____	_____	_____
2.	_____	_____	_____	_____
3.	_____	_____	_____	_____
4.	_____	_____	_____	_____
5.	_____	_____	_____	_____
6.	_____	_____	_____	_____
7.	_____	_____	_____	_____
8.	_____	_____	_____	_____
9.	_____	_____	_____	_____
10.	_____	_____	_____	_____

Part B:
Combine and Create

Making New Words

Directions: Can the prefix be added to the base to make a word? If it can, put an X in the box. If it can't, leave the box blank.

	pre-	*re-*	*un-*
cook			
fold			
heat			
hook			
lock			
pack			
test			
view			

Part C:
Read and Reason

What's the Difference?

Directions: Work with a partner. Write about the differences between these pairs of words.

Word Pair	Differences
precook	
recook	
preview	
review	
refold	
unfold	
pretest	
retest	

Part D:
Extend and Explore

Word Search

Directions: Find the words listed below in the word search. Search diagonally, horizontally, vertically, or backwards.

BACKSTOP   BIRDHOUSE   EVERYDAY
EYEBALL   LOPSIDED   NOSEBLEED
FINGERNAIL   PREPAY   REFUND
FIREFIGHTER   SIDEWALK   UNLOCK

R	D	T	F	R	X	L	N	L	F	P	G	L	K	E
D	N	U	F	E	R	S	R	I	P	O	Q	O	K	G
V	K	R	E	A	R	W	N	C	L	T	V	P	C	B
F	Y	E	P	E	U	G	F	O	G	S	U	S	O	O
P	H	A	M	T	E	W	M	G	X	K	H	I	L	R
S	D	A	P	R	C	O	R	I	K	C	L	D	N	A
E	N	E	N	E	V	E	R	Y	D	A	Y	E	U	N
S	Y	A	E	L	R	A	Y	K	D	B	B	D	U	M
S	I	E	X	L	O	P	L	F	O	K	I	H	U	U
L	C	O	B	J	B	A	X	M	I	N	N	R	F	Z
C	I	B	B	A	W	E	S	U	O	H	D	R	I	B
F	H	Q	H	E	L	U	S	X	T	E	Z	G	L	D
Y	Y	V	D	W	F	L	T	O	R	V	C	D	Q	X
I	F	I	L	Q	B	V	Q	F	N	A	Y	H	G	C
K	S	D	J	R	E	T	H	G	I	F	E	R	I	F

Part E:
Go for the Gold!

Crossword Puzzle

Directions: Read the clues and complete the crossword puzzle.

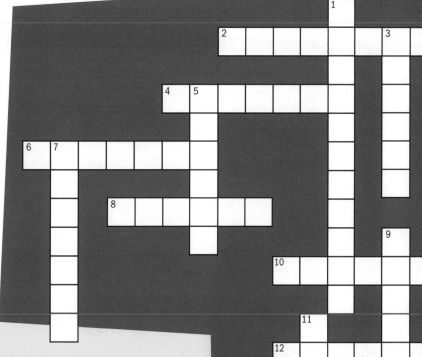

Across
2. crooked
4. small, tasty dessert
6. a look ahead
8. to remove clothes from a bag
10. prepare food ahead of time
12. a way to keep warm when sleeping outside

Down
1. a person who saves burning buildings
3. protection for a valuable body part
5. to open a package
7. check the number
9. an orange swimmer
11. used for transportation

Part A:
Meet the Root

Divide and Conquer

Directions: "Divide" each word into a prefix and a base. Then "conquer" them by writing the meaning of the words.

	prefix means	base is	word means
1. incorrect	not	correct	not correct
2. inexpert			
3. inhuman			
4. insane			
5. insincere			
6. inflexible			
7. infirm			
8. inactive			
9. incomplete			
10. informal			

Part B:
Combine and Create

Solving Riddles

Directions: Solve the riddles with words that begin with *in-*.

1. I mean "wrong."

   I have three syllables. _____

2. I mean "something that is stiff and cannot be bent."

   An example of me is concrete.

   I have four syllables. _____

3. I mean "something you cannot see."

   My opposite is "visible."

   I have four syllables. _____

4. I mean "something that is not finished."

   An example of me is a house that doesn't

   have a roof.

   I have three syllables. _____

Part C:
Read and Reason

"The Indirect (not direct) I'm Sorry"

Directions: Read the poem. Then write a story to describe what happens in the poem. Use prefixes correctly in your story.

I'm in trouble when
Mom calls me "Mister." Mom says,
"Hey, that's indecent, Mister."
"Not decent, Mister, that's
what you are, Mister."
I say, "Mom, you're incorrect!
Not the right answer."
"Invalid answer, Mister.
Not valid.
Not correct?
Your own mother?"
Yikes, Yikes, I think.
I'm in trouble now.
I add, "Please don't be
indirect.
I don't get it—
be direct with what you mean, Mom.
What did I do wrong?"

"You, you, you, Mister,
are intolerant.
Not following the rules again.
Not tolerant."
She sighs, "Inexpert, you are.
Not expert.
Not expert at staying out of trouble,
Mister."
"Mom," I stop.
It's impossible, I think.
Not possible.
"You're right, Mom,
it was improper of me.
Not right.
Not right at all."
I sigh, and offer an indirect
"I'm sorry,"
looking at the floor.

Directions: Work with a partner to write out the story that is told in the poem. Use *in-* words where you can.

_____

_____

_____

_____

Part D:
Extend and Explore

Word Pyramid

Directions: Choose an *in-* word. Work alone or with a partner to make a word pyramid.

Word

Two antonyms

Three synonyms

Definition

Sentence

Part E:
Go for the Gold!

Nine Square Wordo

Directions: This game is like Bingo. First, choose a free box and mark it with an X. Then choose eight of the twelve words from the word list provided by your teacher and write one word in each box. You can choose the box for each word. Then, your teacher will give a clue for each word. Make an X in the box for each word you match to the clue. If you get three words in a row, column, or diagonal, call out, "Wordo!"

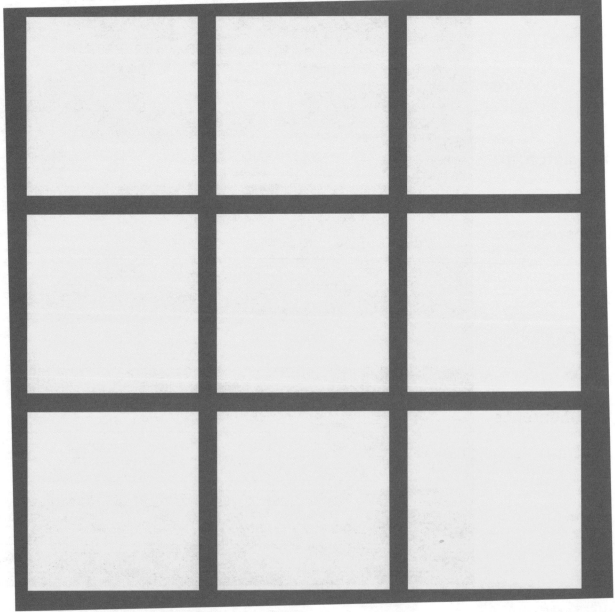

Divide and Conquer

Directions: "Divide" words into prefixes and base words. Then "conquer" them by writing the meaning of the words.

	prefix means	base is	word means
1. impolite	not	polite	not polite
2. impatient	_____	_____	_____
3. illegal	_____	_____	_____
4. illogical	_____	_____	_____
5. immature	_____	_____	_____
6. illegible	_____	_____	_____
7. immobile	_____	_____	_____
8. illiterate	_____	_____	_____
9. immodest	_____	_____	_____
10. improper	_____	_____	_____

Part B:

Combine and Create

Make-a-Word

Directions: Choose the correct prefix for each of the word definitions below.

Not legible = _____

Not mortal = _____

Not patient = _____

Not perfect = _____

Not legal = _____

Not regular = _____

Not polite = _____

Not pure = _____

Not proper = _____

Fill in the Blanks

Directions: Fill in the blanks for this story with words that make sense.

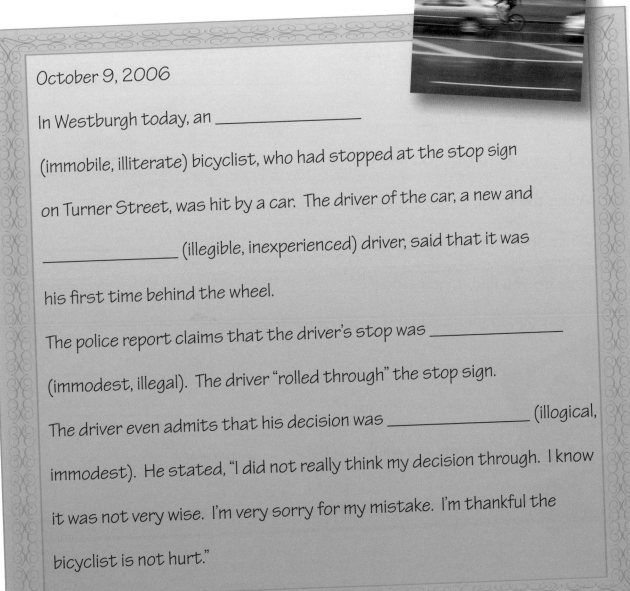

October 9, 2006

In Westburgh today, an _____

(immobile, illiterate) bicyclist, who had stopped at the stop sign

on Turner Street, was hit by a car. The driver of the car, a new and

_____ (illegible, inexperienced) driver, said that it was

his first time behind the wheel.

The police report claims that the driver's stop was _____

(immodest, illegal). The driver "rolled through" the stop sign.

The driver even admits that his decision was _____ (illogical,

immodest). He stated, "I did not really think my decision through. I know

it was not very wise. I'm very sorry for my mistake. I'm thankful the

bicyclist is not hurt."

Part D:
Extend and Explore

Word Questions

Directions: Look over the words in "Divide and Conquer" on page 39.
Then answer these questions.

1. Pick out a word whose meaning you already know.

    Write the word. _____

    What does it mean? _____

2. Pick out a word that you find very interesting, and did not know before.

    Write the word. _____

    What does it mean? _____

    Why do you find it interesting? _____

    3. Pick out a new word that you think is very hard.

        Write the word. _____

        What does it mean? _____

        Tell why you think it is hard. _____

Part E:
Go for the Gold!

Nine Square Wordo

Directions: This game is like Bingo. First, choose a free box and mark it with an X. Then choose eight of the twelve words from the word list provided by your teacher and write one word in each box. You can choose the box for each word. Then, your teacher will give a clue for each word. Make an X in the box for each word you match to the clue. If you get three words in a row, column, or diagonal, call out, "Wordo!"

Part A:
Meet the Root

Divide and Conquer

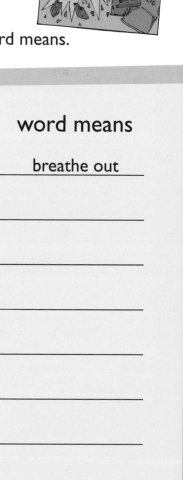

Directions: Read the word. Find the word units.
Write the meaning of each word unit in
the blanks. Then write what the whole word means.

	prefix means	base means	word means
1. expire	out	breathe	breathe out
2. explode		burst	
3. exhale		blow	
4. export		carry	
5. exclude		shut, close	
6. extend		stretch	
7. expose		put, place	
8. expand		spread	
9. exclaim		shout	
10. expense		pay	

Part B:
Combine and Create

Word Forms

Directions: Use other forms of the words to the left to complete the sentences.

Explode

1. I put so much air in the balloon that it _____.
2. When the cannon fired, we could hear the _____ from a mile away.

Explore

1. Astronauts are _____ in outer space.
2. My friend and I _____ the old haunted house.

Expire

1. The _____ date on the milk has passed, so we shouldn't drink it.
2. Before we go to the store, my dad looks to see if our coupons have _____.

Exclaim

1. My teacher says I use too many _____ marks in my writing!
2. Our gym teacher _____, "Let the games begin!"

Directions: Take the prefix off. Then use the base to make another word with *ex-*. Here is an example:

Include =	**in**	+	**clude**	Word with ex-: **exclude**
Inhale =	_____	+	_____	Word with ex-: _____
Import =	_____	+	_____	Word with ex-: _____
Interior =	_____	+	_____	Word with ex-: _____
Internal =	_____	+	_____	Word with ex-: _____

Part C:
Read and Reason

Ex Poetry

Directions: Practice the poem with a partner until you can read it well. You can add motions to the poem. Read it out loud. Use the motions.

Ex- means
Out.
So step out,
Shout out!
Out!
Exclaim
Your
Name.
Shout it,
Out!
Say it
Loud!

Ex- means
Out.
So step out,
Shout out!
Out!
Exhale,
Breathe deep,
Let it out!
Breathe in,
Breathe out,
Who-oo-ee!
Ex- means
Out!
Out!

Part D:
Extend and Explore

Guessing Game

Directions: Work with a partner to complete these sentences by selecting an *ex-* word from the list. You and your partner are a team. Together, choose one of the sentences to read out loud, but skip over the *ex-* word. See if your classmates can guess the missing word.

exclude
exhale   exterior
exhaust   exterminate
exit   extinguish
explode   extinguisher
explore   extend
explorer   expose
export   expense

1. While I was trying to _____

   _____

2. How do you know if _____

   _____

3. Where in the world can _____

   _____

4. What would you think about _____

   _____

5. Why should _____

   _____

Part E:

Go for the Gold!

Nine Square Wordo

Directions: This game is like Bingo. First, choose a free box and mark it with an X. Then choose eight of the twelve words from the word list provided by your teacher and write one word in each box. You can choose the box for each word. Then, your teacher will give a clue for each word. Make an X in the box for each word you match to the clue. If you get three words in a row, column, or diagonal, call out, "Wordo!"

Divide and Conquer

Directions: "Divide" each word into a prefix and a base. The meanings of the bases have been provided. Then "conquer" them by writing the meaning of the words.

	prefix means	base means	word means
1. submarine	under	sea	a boat that travels under sea
2. submerge		plunge	
3. subtract		draw, pull	
4. submit		send	
5. subhuman		human	
6. subtitle		title	
7. subplot		plot	
8. subzero		zero	
9. substandard		standard	
10. subterranean		earth	

Part B:
Combine and Create

Replacement Words

Directions: Replace the bold word in each sentence with a word that begins with *sub-*. Your new sentence might mean something different, but it should still make sense.

1. Let's go downtown on the **bus**. _____

2. In math class, we learn to **add** numbers. _____

3. Tomorrow, we will have **freezing** temperatures. _____

4. Tigers and leopards are both **types** of cats. _____

Directions: Think about the meanings below. Write words that fit the meanings and that begin with *sub-*.

5. Below zero _____

6. Under the surface _____

7. A boat that can go under the sea _____

8. A system of travel that goes underground _____

Directions: *Sub-* can mean "under" or "below." Tell how each of these words has something to do with "under" or "below."

9. Subcommittee _____

10. Subfreezing _____

11. Subsoil _____

12. Substandard _____

Part C:
Read and Reason

Fill in the Blanks

Directions: Choose words from the Word Bank to fill in the blanks for the following journal entry.

October 6, 2006

Dear Diary,

Today at school we learned how to _____, which means to reduce one number from another.

The answer is a lower number. We also learned about the_____, an underground rail system.

We even watched a movie called *The Three Little Pigs*, but it had _____ because the teachers are trying to get us used to Spanish, so they put the words below the picture.

When I got home, I started thinking about my day.

So many words with **sub-** in them. I'll go back to what I wrote above and reread it to try to figure it all out . . .

Sub must mean "beneath" or "below" or something.

Until tomorrow,

Jane

Word Bank

subcommittee
subdivide
subfreezing
subgroup
submarine
subnormal
subsoil
subspecies
substandard
subsurface
subterranean
subtitles
subtract
subtropical
subway
subzero

Part D:
Extend and Explore

Magic Squares

Directions: Work with a partner to complete the magic *sub-* squares. If you are right, the "magic number" will be the same if you add across or down.

A. submerge	1 "under" the main heading
B. substitute	2 transportation "under" the ground
C. substandard	3 stand "under" for something else
D. subway	4 transportation "under" the water
E. submarine	5 "under" the usual quality
F. subfreezing	6 dirt layer "under" the grass
G. subsoil	7 push "under"
H. subtropical	8 "under" hot
I. subtitle	9 "under" cold

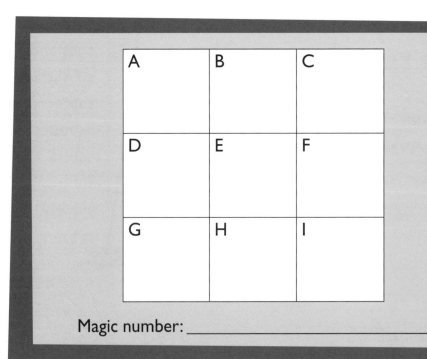

A	B	C
D	E	F
G	H	I

Magic number: _____

Part E:
Go for the Gold!

Nine Square Wordo

Directions: This game is like Bingo. First, choose a free box and mark it with an X. Then choose eight of the twelve words from the word list provided by your teacher and write one word in each box. You can choose the box for each word. Then, your teacher will give a clue for each word. Make an X in the box for each word you match to the clue. If you get three words in a row, column, or diagonal, call out, "Wordo!"

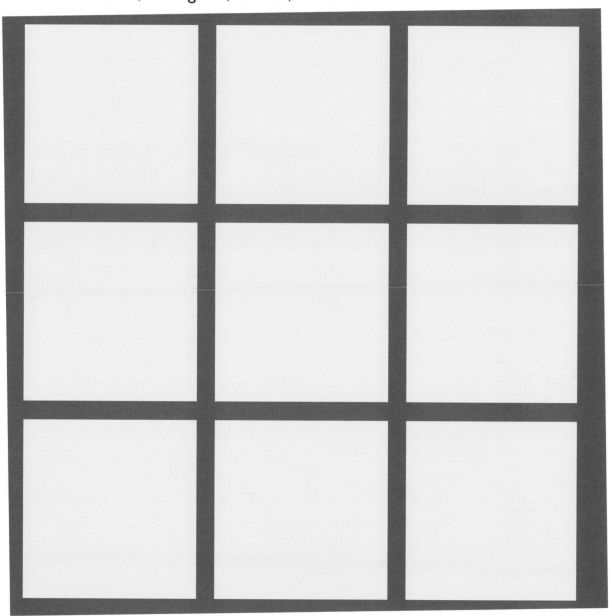

Part A:
Meet the Root

Divide and Conquer

Directions: "Divide" each word into a prefix and a base.
The meanings of the bases have been provided.
Then "conquer" them by writing the meaning of the words.

	prefix means	base means	word means
1. conserve	with	save, keep	keep or save something
2. contract	_____	pull, draw	_____
3. conduct	_____	lead	_____
4. convene	_____	come	_____
5. coauthor	_____	author	_____
6. cooperate	_____	work	_____
7. construct	_____	build	_____
8. convert	_____	turn	_____
9. concoct	_____	cook	_____
10. coexist	_____	live	_____

© *Teacher Created Materials*

Part B:
Combine and Create

Odd Word Out

Directions: Work with a partner to decide which word in each set doesn't belong. Cross it out. Then write your reasons on the lines.

codefendant   cohesive   cosponsor   coworker

_____

_____

_____

coalition   collection   confer   conference

_____

_____

_____

conduct   collect   cosign   cozy

_____

_____

_____

Part C:
Read and Reason

Poem

Directions: Practice the poem below several times by yourself and with a partner. Then write a paragraph that tells the main idea of the poem and describes activities that you can do with others.

COOPERATION
Cooperate, cooperate, confer, and convene.
Let's get together and work as a team.
When we contract to construct and concoct,
We're coworkers, birds of a feather, in the same flock!

_____

_____

_____

_____

_____

_____

_____

Part D:
Extend and Explore

Matching Definitions

Directions: Work with a partner to match these *co-* and *con-* words with their definitions.

concentrate	made from lots of different things
concoction	live side-by-side
conduct	pay close attention
conference	to lead a band
coauthor	agreement
coincidence	clot
coexist	opposite
coagulate	written by more than one person
contract	have a meeting
contrast	happen unexpectedly

Now work with a partner to make up your own matches. Think of words that use the prefixes *re-, ex-,* or *sub-*. Choose eight words. Write them in the left column. Write their definitions on one of the lines in the right-hand column. Make sure to mix up the definitions. Then trade papers with a friend and see if you can "make a match" with each other's lists.

_____	_____
_____	_____
_____	_____
_____	_____
_____	_____
_____	_____
_____	_____

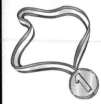

Part E:
Go for the Gold!

Nine Square Wordo

Directions: This game is like Bingo. First, choose a free box and mark it with an X.
Then choose eight of the twelve words from the word list provided by your
teacher and write one word in each box. You can choose the box for each
word. Then, your teacher will give a clue for each word. Make an X in the
box for each word you match to the clue. If you get three words in a row,
column, or diagonal, call out, "Wordo!"

#10653 Building Vocabulary from Word Roots   © *Teacher Created Materials*

Part A:
Meet the Root

Divide and Conquer

Directions: Your teacher will give you a list of words. "Divide" each word into a prefix and a base. Then "conquer" them by writing the meaning of the words.

word	prefix means	base means	word means
1. City			
2.			
3.			
4.			
5.			
6.			
7.			
8.			
9.			
10.			

Part B:
Combine and Create

Writing New Words

Directions: Which of these prefixes can you add to the bases? Write the new words on the lines.

Prefixes: *in-, im-, il-, ex-, sub-, co-, con-*

1. -tract _____

2. -hale _____

3. -clude _____

Select one of the bases above. Work with a partner to make a word web.
First, brainstorm all the words you can think of that have that word part.
Then group the words together. Finally, make a word web.

Part C:
Read and Reason

Word Ladder: Subtract

Directions: Follow the directions to complete the word ladder below.

1. Write the word *subtract*. _____

2. Take off the prefix. _____

3. Replace one letter to make a word that means "draw over lightly."

   _____

4. Remove one letter to make a word that means "a contest."

   _____

5. Remove one letter to name a playing card. _____

6. Change one letter to complete this drink: *lemon* ___ ___ ___

7. Change one letter to make
   the opposite of #1. _____

Part D:
Extend and Explore

Word Search

Directions: Find the words listed below in the word search. Search diagonally, horizontally, vertically, or backwards.

COHABIT
INTOLERANT
INCORRECT
IMMOBILE

EXPIRE
CONCOCT
SUBCOMMITTEE
INFINITE

IMPOLITE
EXPORT
COORDINATE
SUBSTANDARD

T	C	E	R	R	O	C	N	I	F	V	B	Z	P	E
X	E	P	Y	U	D	E	D	K	S	O	X	R	C	L
R	E	U	B	U	W	Q	M	W	T	B	I	O	L	I
A	F	T	A	U	Q	Q	G	Z	Y	N	O	K	J	B
G	S	K	I	Y	P	I	B	N	K	R	O	R	I	O
S	W	U	D	L	E	U	D	I	D	Y	E	S	N	M
Y	S	U	B	C	O	M	M	I	T	T	E	E	T	M
C	J	Q	P	S	V	P	N	I	I	H	G	G	O	I
I	O	W	Y	D	T	A	M	N	A	U	M	U	L	G
U	S	N	S	A	T	A	I	I	D	E	E	V	E	Y
S	A	L	C	E	Q	F	N	O	E	X	L	S	R	G
Q	O	Y	A	O	N	E	T	D	P	P	G	S	A	K
D	D	K	Q	I	C	Z	M	O	A	I	Y	N	N	D
Q	X	N	N	A	T	R	Z	C	R	J	I	T	Y	
C	O	H	A	B	I	T	R	F	C	E	D	B	O	E

Crossword Puzzle

Directions: Read the clues and complete the crossword puzzle.

Across

2. to be unfair to a group of people
3. rude
7. not able to move
8. on the outside
9. to mix together
10. not exactly right

Down

1. a transportation vessel that travels under water
2. the problem of not being able to read
4. to work together
5. against the law
6. to go out
7. crazy

Part A:
Meet the Root

Divide and Conquer

Directions: "Divide" words into base words and prefixes. Some of the words do not have prefixes. Identify those words by marking an X in the column. Then "conquer" them by writing the meaning of the words.

	prefix means	base means	word means
1. visual	X	see	something you see
2. invisible	_____	_____	_____
3. video	_____	_____	_____
4. provide	_____	_____	_____
5. advisor	_____	_____	_____
6. evidence	_____	_____	_____
7. vista	_____	_____	_____
8. visit	_____	_____	_____
9. revise	_____	_____	_____
10. evident	_____	_____	_____

Part B:
Combine and Create

Related Words

Directions: Tell how each of these words has something to do with seeing.

television _____

_____

visible_____

_____

invisible _____

_____

_____

video game _____

_____

_____

_____

DID YOU KNOW?

When television was first invented, it had no name. The word *television* was formed by putting together the Greek root *tele-* which means "from afar," with the Latin base *vis*, which means to "see." The invention of television lets us "see" things that are happening far away (from afar). The word *television* comes from both Greek and Latin. Because its roots are in two languages, we call it a "hybrid" word!

Part C:
Read and Reason

Fill in the Blanks

Directions: Fill in the blanks for this story with words that make sense.

Dear Diary,

My _____ (advisor, supervise)

at school today said that I must start to

_____ (visualize, television) my future.

He asked me what I like to study. I like to do

_____ (videoart, visit), where I

can record things and play them back. Someday, I want

to learn how to make movies to create my own

_____ (vision, visor) of how I see the

world. I also like to watch _____

(video camera, television), and play _____

(videogames, video screens), but that is

after school for fun!

Part D:
Extend and Explore

Word Clues

Directions: Read the clues, and then write the correct words.

A. A six-letter word that means "seeing" or "sight."

B. Add a two-letter prefix to make a new word that means "seeing again." This might describe a piece of your writing that you changed.

C. Take off the prefix from B. Add a new one that has four letters and two syllables. Make a word that names something to watch.

D. Take off the prefix from C. Add a new one that has five letters and two syllables. Make a word that means "overseeing" or "being the boss of others."

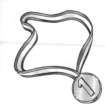

Part E:
Go for the Gold!

Nine Square Wordo

Directions: This game is like Bingo. First, choose a free box and mark it with an X.
Then choose eight of the twelve words from the word list provided by your
teacher and write one word in each box. You can choose the box for each
word. Then, your teacher will give a clue for each word. Make an X in the
box for each word you match to the clue. If you get three words in a row,
column, or diagonal, call out, "Wordo!"

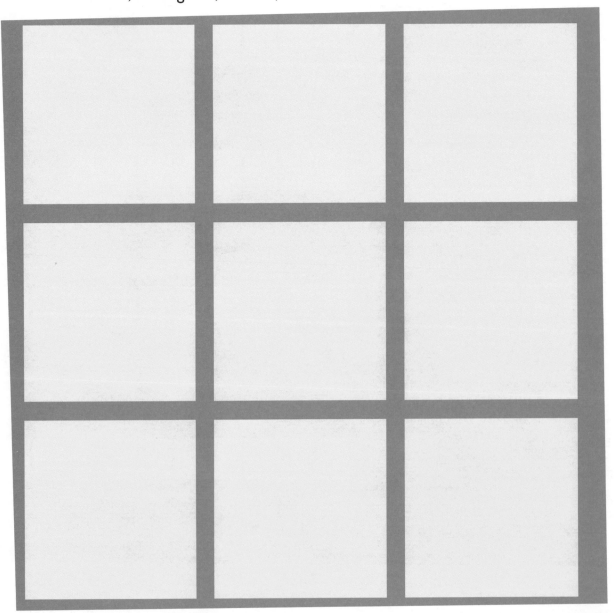

Part A:
Meet the Root

Divide and Conquer

Directions: "Divide" words into base words and prefixes. Not all words in the list have a prefix. Identify those words by marking an X in the column. Then "conquer" them by writing the meaning of the words.

	prefix means	base means	word means
1. export	out	carry	carry out
2. portable			
3. porter			
4. transport			
5. support			
6. report			
7. import			
8. portal			
9. portage			
10. deport			

Part B:
Combine and Create

Word Chart

Directions: Fill in the chart with as many *port* words as you can that start with each of these prefixes.

de-	im-	ex-	trans-

DID YOU KNOW?

The word *portage* comes to us from French explorers who came to North America over 500 years ago. When these explorers moved from rivers to land, they "portaged" (carried) their canoes between bodies of water. Originally, the word portage was from Latin and described ancient Roman soldiers who were exploring the country of France, which they had conquered. It is interesting to see how "portable" the Latin base *port* has become. The Romans "carried" it to France, and the French "carried" it to the New World!

Part C:
Read and Reason

The Harbor

Directions: Read the short story below and circle every word that has *port* in it. (Hint: There are 11 of them!) Then answer the questions that follow.

Look at all the hustle and bustle in the harbor. Ships are docking in the port and unloading all their imported goods. Porters are dashing about and carrying their wares to ships that will export them to other countries. A bus has transported some people from the city down to the dock. Some of the people need support from the driver as they get off the bus with portable luggage that is hard to carry. Before they can board the ship, they must stop and check their luggage at the gate. They do not check their important papers, however, because they keep them in portfolios, which they tuck under their arms. A reporter is taking notes on this busy scene. She will present her report of the busy harbor on the television news that night.

1. What is the difference between *import* and *export?* _____

   _____

2. Write one sentence that describes the word *portfolio*. Make sure you include the word *carry*. _____

   _____

3. Use the words *transport* or *transportation* in a sentence of your own.

   _____

4. Bonus: Native Americans "portaged" their canoes from one river to another. What do you think *portage* means? _____

   _____

Part D:
Extend and Explore

Authors and Illustrators

Directions: You and a partner will be a team. Write a story together using all of these words. You may use the words in any order you want, but you need to use them all.

reporter
television
explode
submarine
export
concentrate
exhale
revisit
support
untidy

Now trade stories with another team. Read their story and draw a picture about some part of the story. Share your illustration and explain what you drew and why. Listen as the other team shares what they drew and why.

#10653 *Building Vocabulary from Word Roots*

Part E:
Go for the Gold!

Nine Square Wordo

Directions: This game is like Bingo. First, choose a free box and mark it with an X. Then choose eight of the twelve words from the word list provided by your teacher and write one word in each box. You can choose the box for each word. Then, your teacher will give a clue for each word. Make an X in the box for each word you match to the clue. If you get three words in a row, column, or diagonal, call out, "Wordo!"

Part A:
Meet the Root

Divide and Conquer

Directions: "Divide" words into base words and prefixes. Not all words will have a prefix. Identify those words by marking an X in the column. Then "conquer" them by writing the meaning of the words.

	prefix means	base means	word means
1. finish	X	end	to get to the end
2. final			
3. refinish			
4. unfinished			
5. finale			
6. infinite			
7. define			
8. fine			
9. refine			
10. confine			

Part B:
Combine and Create

Sorting Words

Directions: Work with a partner to cross out the word that doesn't belong. Write your reasons on the lines.

refine   explain   polish

_____

_____

infinite   endless   closed

_____

_____

first   final   last

_____

_____

DID YOU KNOW?

Because a piece of property has boundary lines, the base *fin* can mean a specific area contained within the "end" lines. If you are *confined* to your room, you are forced to live "within" (con) the "ends" of the contained space. Did you realize that when we *define* a word, we are really putting "down" the "limits" of its meaning?

Part C:
Read and Reason

Dictionary Delight

Directions: Read the short story below and answer the questions that follow.

WOW! My dictionary has finally arrived! It looks so fine on my shelf. I ordered it from the Internet because it looked so fine in the ad. I can now define any word I see, even if I don't know it. With my new dictionary, I can find any definition I need. I can even find out if the word has a prefix or Latin base—and what they mean! The dictionary tells me interesting stories about words that I can share with my friends. In fact, I'm confident that my vocabulary will soon become infinite, and I will no longer have to confine myself to asking other people for the definition of words I do not know. Don't get me wrong: my vocabulary is already quite fine, but with my dictionary, I can refine it even more.

1. Why did the student select this dictionary? _____

_____

2. What do you think *refined* means in this context? _____

_____

3. Have you ever *refined* something you said or wrote?

_____

4. What do you think *confine myself* means in this context? _____

_____

Part D:
Extend and Explore

Word Chart

Directions: Work with a partner to put these words on the chart where they belong.

definite	finance	finch	find	final
finery	finicky	finite	infinity	indefinite

has to do with end or limit	does not have to do with end or limit

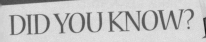

DID YOU KNOW?

When we process things, we start with large pieces and work them down to smaller sizes. The grains on a piece of sandpaper, for example, begin large and coarse. Then they are made smaller for the "medium" grade. At the "end" of the process, the grains are smooth and "fine." The word *fine* in English therefore means "in good condition" because the "end" of processing has been reached. When I *finish* homework and have done a good job, I think my work is fine. We can be in fine health and enjoy a fine meal.

But we can make fine things even better. We can take fine grains of sugar and make them fine "again" by *refining* them! When we *refine* things, we remove all impurities! Manufacturers remove impurities in a *refinery*. You can have fine manners and if you polish them again and again, you can even become a "refined" lady or gentleman!

DID YOU KNOW?

The words *infinite* and *infinity* refer to things so large that they have "no" (negative prefix *in-*) "end." Outer space, for example, extends endlessly. Outer space is infinite because it extends into infinity. The word *infinitesimal*, though, means things that are so tiny they are difficult to measure and see. There seems to be "no" (negative prefix *in-*) "end" to an infinitesimal fraction of a second because it is "endlessly" small.

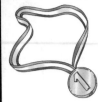

Part E:
Go for the Gold!

Nine Square Wordo

Directions: This game is like Bingo. First, choose a free box and mark it with an X. Then choose eight of the twelve words from the word list provided by your teacher and write one word in each box. You can choose the box for each word. Then, your teacher will give a clue for each word. Make an X in the box for each word you match to the clue. If you get three words in a row, column, or diagonal, call out, "Wordo!"

Part A:
Meet the Root

Divide and Conquer

Directions: "Divide" words into base words and prefixes. Some words may not have prefixes. Identify those words by marking an X in the column. Then "conquer" them by writing the meaning of the words.

	prefix means	base means	word means
1. motion	X	move	movement
2. mobile			
3. remove			
4. motor			
5. remote			
6. motivate			
7. demotion			
8. promotion			
9. movement			
10. movers			

Part B:
Combine and Create

Word Sort

Directions: Put the words on the chart where they belong.

mote	motel	mother	motion
motivate	motorist	motorized	motto

has something to do with moving	does not have something to do with moving

DID YOU KNOW?

The word *motel* is a short form of *motor hotel*. As highways were built across America, more people began to travel. Roadside hotels were built so that travelers would have a place to spend the night. These motor hotels became known as motels because they were designed for people "on the move"!

Part C:
Read and Reason

Story Time

Directions: Read the following stories and answer the questions.

Davey felt unmotivated to do his homework. So he decided to ride his motorcycle to the store. The motion of the bike made him feel free as he glided through the air without a helmet (which his mother always wanted him to wear).

Question:

What do you think *mot* means in the story above? _____

_____

_____

I was sitting in my family room, watching TV and flipping channels with the remote when the new soda commercial came on TV. The commercial was promotional in nature and went out of its way to claim that the soda was better tasting than before. Before it was over, I changed the channel to a new sports show for water enthusiasts—a motorboat race down the Mississippi River.

Question:

How is *mot* used in the above story? _____

_____

_____

Question:

Which *mot* word in the story do you like the best? Explain why. _____

_____

_____

Part D:
Extend and Explore

Charting Words

Directions: Work with a partner to fill in the chart. Some boxes may have more than one word. Some boxes may be blank.

	-mote	-motion	-ed	-ing
com-				
de-				
pro-				
re-				

Part E:
Go for the Gold!

Nine Square Wordo

Directions: This game is like Bingo. First, choose a free box and mark it with an X.
Then choose eight of the twelve words from the word list provided by your
teacher and write one word in each box. You can choose the box for each
word. Then, your teacher will give a clue for each word. Make an X in the
box for each word you match to the clue. If you get three words in a row,
column, or diagonal, call out, "Wordo!"

Part A:
Meet the Root

Divide and Conquer

Directions: "Divide" words into base words and prefixes. Some words may not have prefixes. Write an X on the line if the word does not have a prefix. Then "conquer" them by writing the meaning of the words.

	prefix means	base means	word means
1. graph	X	draw	a drawing that represents information
2. autograph	_____	_____	_____
3. biography	_____	_____	_____
4. telegram	_____	_____	_____
5. grammar	_____	_____	_____
6. phonograph	_____	_____	_____
7. graphite	_____	_____	_____
8. diagram	_____	_____	_____
9. photograph	_____	_____	_____
10. autobiography	_____	_____	_____

Part B:
Combine and Create

Fill in the Blanks

Directions: Tell about the people who have these jobs. Use these words:

biography, biographer, calligraphy, calligrapher, stenography, stenographer

I write for a living. It takes me a very long time to write something because I use very fancy and beautiful letters.

I am a _____ .

My job is called _____ .

I also write for a living. Sometimes I work in offices, but I also work in the courts. My job is to take down everything that everyone says. I need to write very quickly and in narrow (Greek *steno-*) columns.

I am a _____ .

My job is called _____ .

I write for a living too. I must do a lot of research before I write. My job is to write down the story of someone's life.

I am a _____ .

My job is called writing a _____ .

Part C:
Read and Reason

Fill in the Blanks

Directions: Fill in the blanks with words that make sense.

On a trip to Hollywood, I ran into a couple of

celebrities. I asked each of them for an

_____ (paragraph, autograph). One

celebrity told me that his _____ (biographer,

phonograph), the guy who writes about his life, was coming out with a new

_____ (biography, stenography) about him, and I should

pick it up. Another one told me that I was truly getting a _____

(geography, graphic) lesson traveling out here from Ohio.

DID YOU KNOW?

The word *paragraph* originally referred to a P-shaped letter that was placed in the margin of a text as a sign for the printer to indent at that spot. The Greek prefix *para-* means "alongside." A paragraph was therefore originally just a mark "written" (graph) "alongside" (para-) the text, telling the printer where to indent.

Part D:
Extend and Explore

Letter Scramble

Directions: Unscramble the words to fit in the story. Write the unscrambled word on the correct line.

1. AAGHOPRTU
2. ABIGHOPRY

3. AAAGHPPRRS
4. ABEGHIOPRR

When I am a famous baseball player, people will want my (1)_____. I know that

some players charge money for these, but I won't. I will be happy that people want them.

I also plan to have someone write my (2) _____. Right now, this would only be a

few (3) _____ long, but that's because I'm still a child. When I get to be a

famous baseball player, my (4) _____ will have lots more to tell about.

Think of five *graph* or *gram* words. Scramble one on each line. Then trade with a neighbor and try to unscramble each other's words!

1. Word is _____

2. Word is _____

3. Word is _____

4. Word is _____

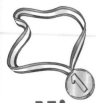

Part E:
Go for the Gold!

Nine Square Wordo

Directions: This game is like Bingo. First, choose a free box and mark it with an X.
Then choose eight of the twelve words from the word list provided by your
teacher and write one word in each box. You can choose the box for each
word. Then, your teacher will give a clue for each word. Make an X in the
box for each word you match to the clue. If you get three words in a row,
column, or diagonal, call out, "Wordo!"

Part A:
Meet the Root

Divide and Conquer

Directions: Your teacher will give you a list of words. "Divide" each word into a prefix and a base. Then "conquer" them by writing the meaning of the words.

word	prefix means	base means	word means
1.			
2.			
3.			
4.			
5.			
6.			
7.			
8.			
9.			
10.			

Part B:
Combine and Create

Word Play

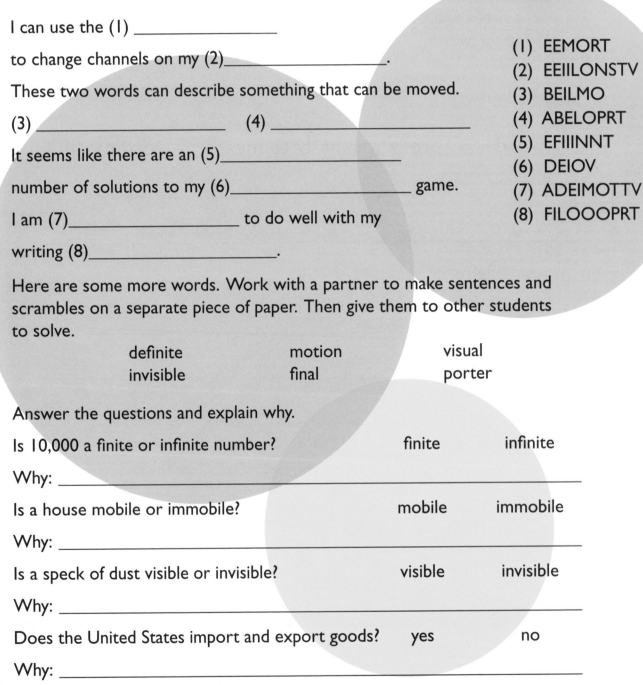

Directions: Unscramble the letters to make words that go in the sentences.

I can use the (1) _____

to change channels on my (2)_____.

These two words can describe something that can be moved.

(3) _____   (4) _____

It seems like there are an (5)_____

number of solutions to my (6)_____ game.

I am (7)_____ to do well with my

writing (8)_____.

(1) EEMORT
(2) EEIILONSTV
(3) BEILMO
(4) ABELOPRT
(5) EFIIINNT
(6) DEIOV
(7) ADEIMOTTV
(8) FILOOOPRT

Here are some more words. Work with a partner to make sentences and scrambles on a separate piece of paper. Then give them to other students to solve.

definite   motion   visual
invisible   final   porter

Answer the questions and explain why.

Is 10,000 a finite or infinite number?   finite   infinite

Why: _____

Is a house mobile or immobile?   mobile   immobile

Why: _____

Is a speck of dust visible or invisible?   visible   invisible

Why: _____

Does the United States import and export goods?   yes   no

Why: _____

Fill in the Blanks

Directions: Read the story and fill in the blanks with words from the Word Bank.

Word Bank
imports
importing   portable
exports   support
exporter   porter
deports   transporting
deportation   transportation
ports

The United States _____

and _____ many goods every

year, carrying them into and out of

the country on a regular basis on

different _____ vehicles.

During the peak season of Christmas, the _____ are

crowded with merchandise, especially toys. Every _____

ends up working longer hours and getting ready for the big

rush.

Part D:

Extend and Explore

Word Skits

Directions: Work with a partner.
First, pick a word.

Then write it on an index card. Write what it means, and write an example of when you might see it.

Tell classmates what root you have used.

Then act out the example of when you might see the word. See if your classmates can guess the word.

Words: television motorcycle reporter definite

Part E:
Go for the Gold!

Word Search

Directions: Find the words listed below in the word search. Search diagonally, horizontally, vertically, or backwards.

CONFINE	DEFINE	DIAGRAM
EMOTION	FINAL	INFINITE
MOBILE	MOTOR	PARAGRAPH
PROMOTE	REPORTER	

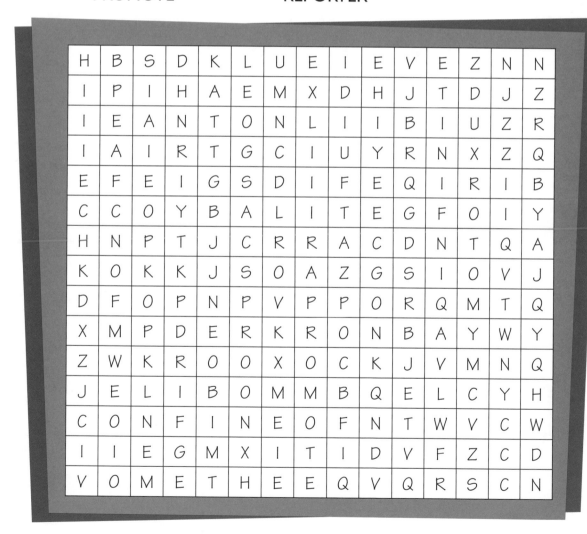

H	B	S	D	K	L	U	E	I	E	V	E	Z	N	N
I	P	I	H	A	E	M	X	D	H	J	T	D	J	Z
I	E	A	N	T	O	N	L	I	I	B	I	U	Z	R
I	A	I	R	T	G	C	I	U	Y	R	N	X	Z	Q
E	F	E	I	G	S	D	I	F	E	Q	I	R	I	B
C	C	O	Y	B	A	L	I	T	E	G	F	O	I	Y
H	N	P	T	J	C	R	R	A	C	D	N	T	Q	A
K	O	K	K	J	S	O	A	Z	G	S	I	O	V	J
D	F	O	P	N	P	V	P	P	O	R	Q	M	T	Q
X	M	P	D	E	R	K	R	O	N	B	A	Y	W	Y
Z	W	K	R	O	O	X	O	C	K	J	V	M	N	Q
J	E	L	I	B	O	M	M	B	Q	E	L	C	Y	H
C	O	N	F	I	N	E	O	F	N	T	W	V	C	W
I	I	E	G	M	X	I	T	I	D	V	F	Z	C	D
V	O	M	E	T	H	E	E	Q	V	Q	R	S	C	N

Part A:
Meet the Root

Divide and Conquer

Directions: "Divide" words into base words and suffixes.
Then "conquer" them by writing the meaning of the words.

	base is	suffix means	word means
1. wireless	wire	without	without a wire
2. hopeless			
3. powerless			
4. joyless			
5. endless			
6. homeless			
7. worthless			
8. painless			
9. colorless			
10. seedless			

Part B:
Combine and Create

Word Sort

Directions: Look at these groups of words. Find the one that doesn't belong.
Explain why.

hitless   homeless   hopeless

The word_____ doesn't belong because

_____

hopeless   shameless   wireless

The word_____ doesn't belong because

_____

seedless   sleepless   sugarless

The word_____ doesn't belong because

_____

Part C:
Read and Reason

News Story

Directions: Choose words from the Word Bank to fill in the blanks for the following news story. Then answer the questions.

Word Bank

blameless	breathless
careless	colorless
endless	homeless
hopeless	reckless
seedless	shameless

LOCAL NEWS

IN BRIEF (MORE IS LESS)

Today, in Unhappyville, _____ citizens protested at city hall. Their main complaint is there are no programs to help find them homes. Harvey Power-less says, "Life seems _____ when no one wants to help." And, even though the struggle seems _____ (with no end in sight), Powerless goes on to say, "I feel like the people will start to listen when they hear of our problems. I don't think people know how they can help. I want to tell them."

Questions

1. What does it mean if someone is *homeless*? _____

   _____

2. What are three things Harvey Powerless can do to help homeless citizens feel hopeful? _____

   _____

   _____

Part D:
Extend and Explore

Solving Riddles

Directions: Solve the riddles. (Hint: All answers will end in -*less*.)

1. I am a feeling that happens when you huff and puff.
    You would feel like me if you ran very fast for a long time.
    I have ten letters but only three vowels.

    _____

2. I mean "very, very still."
    I mean "without moving."
    I have three syllables.

    _____

3. I describe what you would be if you stayed up all night.
    I have one vowel used three times.
    I also have the letter **s** used three times.

    _____

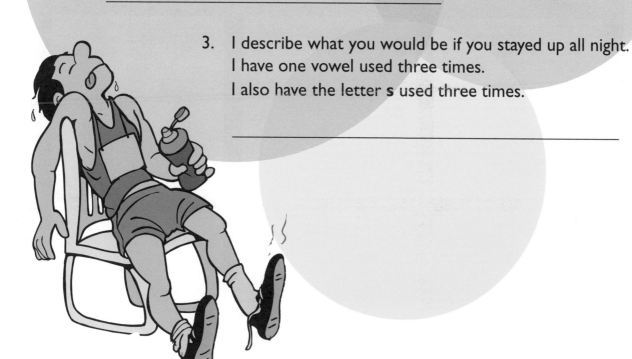

Part E:
Go for the Gold!

Nine Square Wordo

Directions: This game is like Bingo. First, choose a free box and mark it with an X.
Then choose eight of the twelve words from the word list provided by your
teacher and write one word in each box. You can choose the box for each
word. Then, your teacher will give a clue for each word. Make an X in the
box for each word you match to the clue. If you get three words in a row,
column, or diagonal, call out, "Wordo!"

Part A:
Meet the Root

Divide and Conquer

Directions: "Divide" words into base words and suffixes. Then "conquer" them by writing the meaning of the new word.

	base is	suffix means	word means
1. colorful	color	full of	full of color
2. joyful	_____	_____	_____
3. playful	_____	_____	_____
4. hateful	_____	_____	_____
5. wonderful	_____	_____	_____
6. truthful	_____	_____	_____
7. powerful	_____	_____	_____
8. wasteful	_____	_____	_____
9. beautiful	_____	_____	_____
10. hopeful	_____	_____	_____

Part B:
Combine and Create

Find and Replace

Directions: Replace the underlined words in each sentence with one word that ends in *-ful*.

1. My new coat is <u>full of color</u>.

   _____

2. When I play with my baby sister, I am <u>full of care</u>.

   _____

3. The salad we made for dinner was <u>full of flavor</u>.

   _____

4. After the storm, we saw a rainbow that was <u>full of beauty</u>.

   _____

Part C:
Read and Reason

Conversation Words

Directions: Fill in the blanks for this conversation with the words that make sense. Then read it out loud with a friend. Make sure to read your part with expression!

Steve: Hey Jessica! How are you today?

Jessica: I'm pretty good. Well, to be _____ (truthful, wasteful), I'm feeling great.

Steve: Do you find it _____ (stressful, joyful) thinking about our upcoming math test?

Jessica: I'm feeling pretty good about it. But it's always good to be cautious. I should be _____ (wonderful, careful) about what I say. I feel _____ (hopeful, painful) that I'll be relaxed since I've been doing my homework.

Steve: Are you going to study?

Jessica: Of course! I want to make sure I do well, and being _____ (shameful, faithful) about my studying will help me feel good and have fun with it.

Part D:
Extend and Explore

Describing Words

Directions: Work with a partner. First, think of three things that these words can describe. Then write a sentence about your reasons.

1. Powerful _____   _____   _____

   These things are powerful because _____

   _____

2. Colorful _____   _____   _____

   These things are colorful because _____

   _____

3. Playful _____   _____   _____

   These things are playful because _____

   _____

4. Wonderful _____   _____   _____

   These things are wonderful because _____

   _____

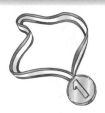

Part E:
Go for the Gold!

Nine Square Wordo

Directions: This game is like Bingo. First, choose a free box and mark it with an X. Then choose eight of the twelve words from the word list provided by your teacher and write one word in each box. You can choose the box for each word. Then, your teacher will give a clue for each word. Make an X in the box for each word you match to the clue. If you get three words in a row, column, or diagonal, call out, "Wordo!"

Part A:
Meet the Root

Divide and Conquer

Directions: "Divide" words into base adjectives and suffixes. Then "conquer" them by writing the meaning of the words.

	base adjective	suffix means	word means
1. smarter	smart	more	more smart than another
2. quicker			
3. smaller			
4. prettier			
5. earlier			
6. greater			
7. richer			
8. poorer			
9. busier			
10. saltier			

Part B:
Combine and Create

Spelling Practice

Directions: When a word ends in *y*, change the *y* to an *i* before adding *-er*. For example, "more easy" = easier. Make *-er* words from these words that end in *y*. Then write a sentence using each word.

1. Ugly _____

   Sentence _____

   _____

2. Angry _____

   Sentence _____

   _____

3. Early _____

   Sentence _____

   _____

4. Roomy _____

   Sentence _____

   _____

5. Pretty _____

   Sentence _____

   _____

Part C:
Read and Reason

Fill in the Blanks

Directions: Choose words from the Word Bank to fill in the blanks for the following story. Some of the words will be used twice.

The Knight of the Round Table felt even _____

after he defeated the dragon Red Beard. And he reflected back on

how he had slayed the savage beast.

First, he had walked _____ and _____
(same word for both blanks)

into the dragon's cave. And as he approached _____ and
(same word for both blanks)

_____, he began to hear the dragon breathing deeply.

Slow and steady. Slow and steady.

But then the dragon's breath became _____. The

knight knew he was in trouble. He brought out his bow and arrow.

He fit the arrow into the notch and pulled the string back.

He watched as the arrow rose _____ and _____
(same word for both blanks)

into the air, finally going down and landing in the

dragon. He closed his eyes.

Word Bank
angrier
braver
deeper
earlier
greater
higher
nearer
poorer
prettier
roomier
faster

Word Sort

Directions: Sometimes -er means "more," and sometimes it doesn't (-er means "more" only when attached to an adjective). Put each word on the chart where it belongs.

| batter | deeper | driver | faster | harder | higher |
| greater | maker | rider | runner | slower | worker |

-er means "more"	-er doesn't mean "more"

Choose an -er word from your chart. Make a word pyramid based on that -er word, but don't fill in the top line. Start with two antonyms and work your way down.

Word _____

Two Antonyms _____ _____

Three Synonyms _____ _____ _____

Definition _____

Sentence _____

Trade pyramids with a friend and see if you can each figure out the -er word from the clues. Write the -er word on the top line.

Part E:
Go for the Gold!

Nine Square Wordo

Directions: This game is like Bingo. First, choose a free box and mark it with an X. Then choose eight of the twelve words from the word list provided by your teacher and write one word in each box. You can choose the box for each word. Then, your teacher will give a clue for each word. Make an X in the box for each word you match to the clue. If you get three words in a row, column, or diagonal, call out, "Wordo!"

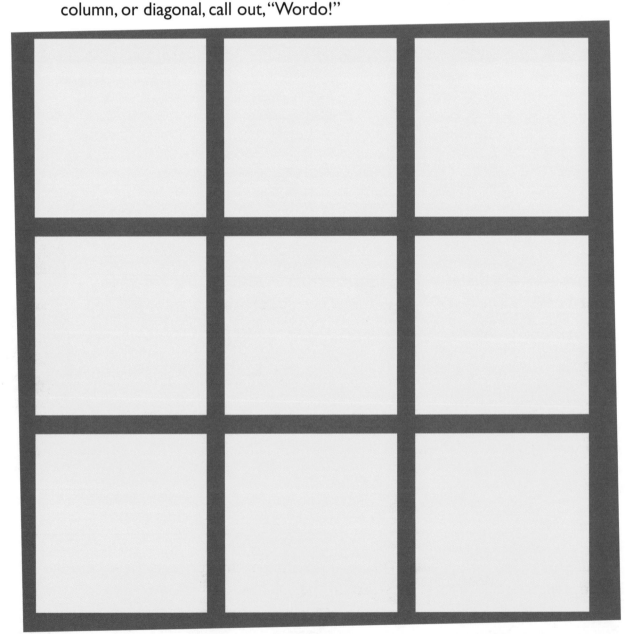

#10653 Building Vocabulary from Word Roots

Part A:
Meet the Root

Divide and Conquer

Directions: "Divide" words into base adjectives and suffixes.
Then "conquer" them by writing the meaning of
the words.

	base adjective	suffix means	word means
1. wisest	wise	most	most wise
2. prettiest			
3. quickest			
4. slowest			
5. smartest			
6. laziest			
7. bravest			
8. richest			
9. angriest			
10. happiest			

Part B:
Combine and Create

Descriptive Words

Directions: Work with a partner. Write three words ending in -est that could describe:

a person

1. _____

2. _____

3. _____

a rock

1. _____

2. _____

3. _____

an animal

1. _____

2. _____

3. _____

a tree

1. _____

2. _____

3. _____

Part C:
Read and Reason

Adelia's Advice

Directions: Choose words from the Word Bank to fill in the blanks for the following letter written to advice columnist, Adelia Advice.

Dear Adelia Advice,

I met the _____ runner the other day at my cross country meet. He ran faster than anyone on our team, or on any of the other teams. Our coach called him the _____ runner of all time.

So here's my question. I am not the _____ runner on our team, but I could improve. I practice everyday and even get up during the _____ hours of the morning so I can run before school.

What other advice would you have for me to become a better runner? What is your _____ advice?

Concerned Runner

Word Bank

angriest

bravest

deepest

earliest

fastest

hardest

greatest

soonest

wisest

slowest

Part D:
Extend and Explore

Word Sort

Directions: Sometimes -*est* means "most." Sometimes it doesn't (-*est* means "most" only when it is attached to adjectives). Put these words on the correct side of the chart.

best	fastest	greatest	hardest	highest	longest	nearest
nest	pest	poorest	rest	test	west	zest

-*est* means "most"	-*est* doesn't mean "most"

Choose an -*est* word from your chart. Make a word pyramid based on that -*est* word, but don't fill in the top line. Start with two antonyms and work your way down.

Word   _____

Two antonyms   _____   _____

Three synonyms   _____   _____   _____

Definition   _____

Sentence   _____

Trade pyramids with a friend and see if you can each figure out the -*est* word from the clues. Write the -*est* word on the top line.

Part E:
Go for the Gold!

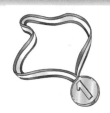

Nine Square Wordo

Directions: This game is like Bingo. First, choose a free box and mark it with an X. Then choose eight of the twelve words from the word list provided by your teacher and write one word in each box. You can choose the box for each word. Then, your teacher will give a clue for each word. Make an X in the box for each word you match to the clue. If you get three words in a row, column, or diagonal, call out, "Wordo!"

Part A:
Meet the Root

Divide and Conquer

Directions: "Divide" words into base adjectives and suffixes. Then "conquer" them by writing the meaning of the words.

	base adjective	suffix means in a way or manner	word means
1. slowly	slow	in a way or manner	in a slow manner
2. merrily			
3. happily			
4. wisely			
5. quickly			
6. gently			
7. softly			
8. carefully			
9. cheaply			
10. lazily			

Part B:
Combine and Create

How Many *Ls*?

Directions: Work with a partner to complete the chart. Think about the spelling of each word when an -*ly* is added to the end.

beautiful	careful	cheap	fatal	free
gentle	manual	perfect	secret	soft

with -*ly* (has one *l*)	with -*ly* (has two *l*s)

Part C:
Read and Reason

Poetry Reading

Directions: Practice reading the following poem with expression.
Then answer the questions.

Break it down.
Know the sound.
Move toward
The definition
Of the word.

Beautifully,
Beautiful,
Beauty,
All mean
The same thing,
Basically.

Carefully,
Careful,
Care,
All mean
The same thing,
Basically.

Break it down.
Know the sound.
Move toward
The definition
Of the word.

Cheaply,
Cheap,
Softly,
Soft.

Break it down.
Know the sound.
Move toward
The definition
Of the word.

Pitifully,
Pitiful,
Gladly,
Glad,
All mean
The same thing,
Basically.

Break it down.
Know the sound.
Move toward
The definition
Of the word.

Questions:

1. How does the addition of -*ly* change the words in the above poem?

_____

_____

2. Choose one of the -*ly* words and write a definition.

_____

_____

Part D:
Extend and Explore

Guess the Word

Directions: Work with a partner to complete these sentences using an -*ly* word from the list below. You and your partner are a team. Together choose one of the sentences to read out loud, but skip over the -*ly* word. See if your classmates can guess the missing word.

greatly   gently   quietly   laughingly   cheaply

painlessly   secretly   perfectly   frankly

immediately   beautifully   favorably   gladly

1. While I was trying to _____

   _____

2. How do you know if _____

   _____

3. Where in the world can_____

   _____

4. What would you think about_____

   _____

5. Why should _____

   _____

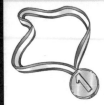

Part E:
Go for the Gold!

Nine Square Wordo

Directions: This game is like Bingo. First, choose a free box and mark it with an X. Then choose eight of the twelve words from the word list provided by your teacher and write one word in each box. You can choose the box for each word. Then, your teacher will give a clue for each word. Make an X in the box for each word you match to the clue. If you get three words in a row, column, or diagonal, call out, "Wordo!"

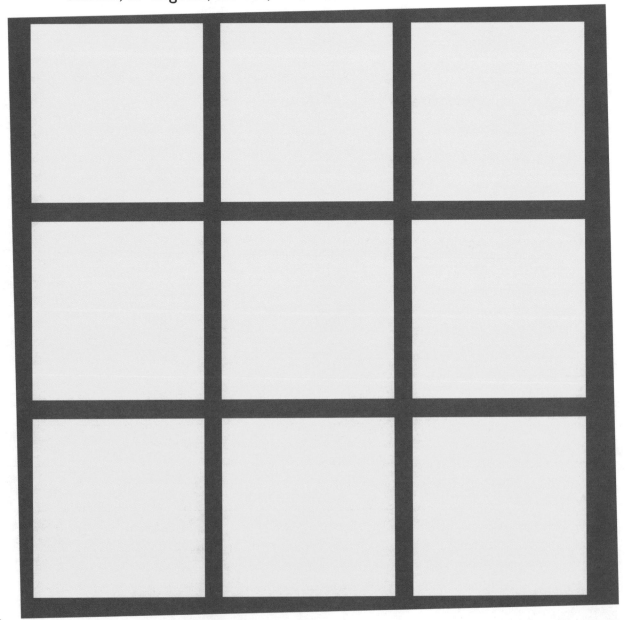

Part A:
Meet the Root

Divide and Conquer

Directions: Your teacher will give you a list of words. "Divide" words into base adjectives and suffixes. Then "conquer" them by writing the meaning of the words.

	word	base adjective	suffix means	word means
1.	_____	_____	_____	_____
2.	_____	_____	_____	_____
3.	_____	_____	_____	_____
4.	_____	_____	_____	_____
5.	_____	_____	_____	_____
6.	_____	_____	_____	_____
7.	_____	_____	_____	_____
8.	_____	_____	_____	_____
9.	_____	_____	_____	_____
10.	_____	_____	_____	_____

Part B:
Combine and Create

Writing New Sentences

Directions: Look at the underlined word. Make the change.
Write a new sentence.

1. My brother is <u>careless</u> with his toys.

   Drop the -*less*. _____

   Add -*ful*. _____

   New sentence: _____

   Add -*fully*. _____

   New sentence: _____

2. The baby thinks her toy bear is <u>silly</u>.

   Add -*er* (Hint: Be careful with the y). _____

   New sentence: _____

   Change the -*er* to -*est*. _____

   New sentence: _____

3. Thank you for the beautiful coat. This is a very <u>thoughtful</u> gift.

   Drop the -*ful*. _____

   Add -*less*. _____

   New sentence: _____

Part C:
Read and Reason

Fairy Tale Writing

Directions: Work with a partner to write a fairy tale. First, think about the topic of your story. What will it be about? Next, go back through "Divide and Conquer" for lessons 16–20 and choose a *-less, -ful, -er, -est,* and *-ly* word that you can use in your story. Then write the story using the outline below. Make sure you use at least one *-less, -ful, -er, -est* and *-ly* word.

Once upon a time _____

_____.

One day _____

_____.

Then _____

_____.

Finally, _____

_____,

and so they _____

_____

Now trade stories with another team. Read each other's story. Find the *-less, -ful, -er, -est,* and *-ly* words in their story, and write them on the blanks below.

_____   _____   _____

_____   _____   _____

_____   _____   _____

Part D:
Extend and Explore

Word Chart

Directions: Work with a partner to complete the chart. Some boxes will remain blank. (Hint: Be careful with words ending in -y.)

	-less	-ful	-er	-est	-ly
care					
quick					
happy					
slow					

Part E:
Go for the Gold!

Word Search

Directions: Find the words in the puzzle. Search diagonally, horizontally, vertically, or backwards. Be careful! Some words start the same.

ANGRIER	ANGRIEST	BEAUTIFUL	BEAUTIFULLY
CAREFUL	CAREFULLY	CARELESS	CARELESSLY
SAFELY	SAFER	SAFEST	TASTEFUL
TASTELESS			

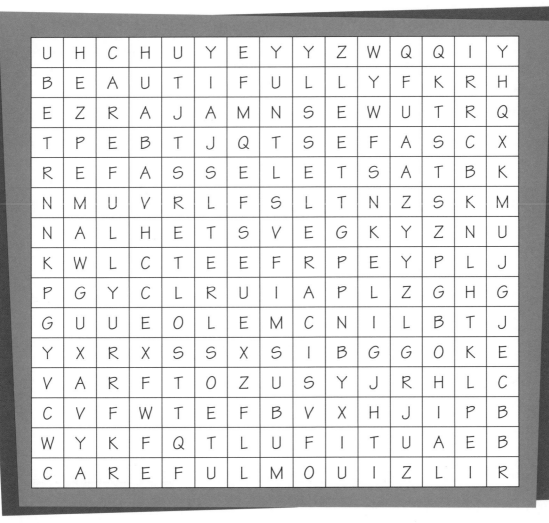

U	H	C	H	U	Y	E	Y	Y	Z	W	Q	Q	I	Y
B	E	A	U	T	I	F	U	L	L	Y	F	K	R	H
E	Z	R	A	J	A	M	N	S	E	W	U	T	R	Q
T	P	E	B	T	J	Q	T	S	E	F	A	S	C	X
R	E	F	A	S	S	E	L	E	T	S	A	T	B	K
N	M	U	V	R	L	F	S	L	T	N	Z	S	K	M
N	A	L	H	E	T	S	V	E	G	K	Y	Z	N	U
K	W	L	C	T	E	E	F	R	P	E	Y	P	L	J
P	G	Y	C	L	R	U	I	A	P	L	Z	G	H	G
G	U	U	E	O	L	E	M	C	N	I	L	B	T	J
Y	X	R	X	S	S	X	S	I	B	G	G	O	K	E
V	A	R	F	T	O	Z	U	S	Y	J	R	H	L	C
C	V	F	W	T	E	F	B	V	X	H	J	I	P	B
W	Y	K	F	Q	T	L	U	F	I	T	U	A	E	B
C	A	R	E	F	U	L	M	O	U	I	Z	L	I	R

Part A:
Meet the Root

Divide and Conquer

Directions: "Divide" words into two parts. There is a Latin number prefix and a base. The bases have been given to you. (Words that do not have a base have an X.) Then "conquer" them by writing the meaning of the words.

		prefix means	base means	word means
1.	uniform	one	*form* = shape	having the same shape, as in clothing
2.	unify		*fy* = make	
3.	unicorn		*corn* = horn	
4.	union		X	
5.	unit		X	
6.	unique		X	
7.	unicycle		*cycle* = wheel	
8.	unisex		*sex* = gender	
9.	unison		*son* = sound	
10.	universe		*vers* = turn	

Part B:
Combine and Create

Solving Riddles

Directions: Solve the word riddles. Each word will start with *uni-*.

1. I am clothes.
    Many people wear me to work, but I always look the same. Firefighters wear me. _____

2. I am a pretend animal.
    I have one horn.
    I mean "one of a kind." _____

3. I have the letters *qu* in me.
    I mean "original."
    I rhyme with "you sneak." _____

4. I am a country.
    I am in North America.
    I have 50 states. _____

DID YOU KNOW?

We arrange large numbers in columns. In numbers with three figures, the first column on the left-hand side is for the "hundreds," the second column is for the "tens," and the third column is for the "units." The "units" in math are for numbers 0 through 9. These are the "ones" because we need only one number to express them! In the number 763, which is the "unit" number?

Part C:
Read and Reason

Fill in the Blanks

Directions: Fill in the blanks for this story of third grader Julio Gonzales who recently moved from Mexico to America. Then answer the questions.

My name is Julio Gonzales. I moved from Mexico to the _____ (Unison States, United States) of America. I am in the third grade at a private school. At the private school, the children wear a _____ (uniform, unit) that consists of black pants and blue shirts. All the boys wear ties, and the girls wear either black pants or black skirts. Soon, I will travel back to Mexico, and all of my family members will get together for a party. We have this family get-together each year, and it is called the Gonzales Family _____ (unify, reunion).

Now, write back to Julio and tell him about yourself. Where do you live? Do you wear a uniform to school? If you do, what does it look like? Does your family have a reunion every year?

Dear Julio,

_____

_____

_____

_____

_____

_____

CANADA

UNITED STATES

MEXICO

Part D:
Extend and Explore

Finish the Sentence

Directions: Work with a partner to find the correct *uni-* or *unit-* word for each sentence. First use what you know to try and figure out any words that are difficult. Then check the dictionary to see how you did. (Hint: One word will be used twice!)

Word Bank
universe
unit
unison
united
uniform
unicycle
unisex
unique
unicorn

1.   The soldiers paraded while dressed in full _____.

2.   This week's _____ is about number words.

3.   A cycle with only one wheel is called a _____.

4.   Men and women get haircuts together at a _____ salon.

5.   The school choir was singing in perfect _____.

6.   The earth and planets revolving together are part of the _____.

7.   In American history, the original 13 colonies joined together to form the _____ States.

8.   No two people look exactly alike, because each person on earth is _____.

9.   A bull has two horns, but a _____ only has one.

10. The clown almost fell off his _____ at the circus.

Part E:
Go for the Gold!

Nine Square Wordo

Directions: This game is like Bingo. First, choose a free box and mark it with an X. Then choose eight of the twelve words from the word list provided by your teacher and write one word in each box. You can choose the box for each word. Then, your teacher will give a clue for each word. Make an X in the box for each word you match to the clue. If you get three words in a row, column, or diagonal, call out, "Wordo!"

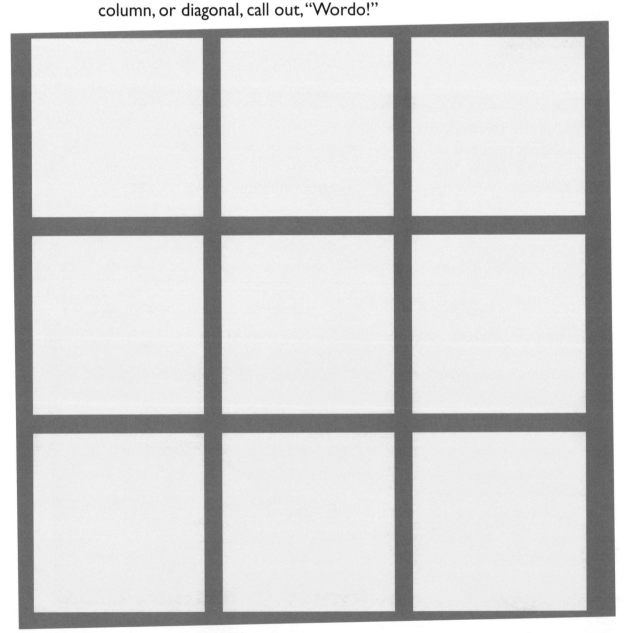

Part A:
Meet the Root

Divide and Conquer

Directions: "Divide" words into two parts. There is a Latin number prefix and a base. The bases have been given to you. Then "conquer" them by writing the meaning of the words.

	prefix means	base means	word means
1. bicycle	two	*cycl* = wheel	a two-wheeled toy to ride
2. biannual		*annu* = year	
3. bimonthly		*month* = month	
4. bisect		*sect* = cut	
5. bilingual		*lingu* = language	
6. binoculars*		*ocul* = eye	
7. bifocal		*foc* = focus	
8. bicolor		*color* = color	
9. biweekly		*week* = week	
10. biped		*ped* = foot	

* In the word *binoculars*, an *n* is placed after *bi-* to make the word easier to pronounce.

Part B:
Combine and Create

Fill in the Blanks

Directions: Fill in the blanks with a word that starts with *bi-*.

1. My house is all on one level. Sam's house has two levels. His house is called

    a _____ house.

2. We went to the air show. We saw lots of airplanes. My favorites were the ones

    with two sets of wings. My mom said they are called _____.

3. My little sister used to ride a tricycle. She's old enough now to ride a

    two-wheeler. On Saturday, she is going to get her first _____.

4. My grandmother recently got new glasses. With her new lenses, she can

    focus on things close up and on things far away. She got her first pair

    of _____.

5. We use a telescope to look at the stars and other things that are very

    far away. But birdwatchers prefer to use _____.

6. Maria's parents came to the United States from Mexico. They speak

    perfect English and have not forgotten their Spanish. Maria's household

    is _____.

Part C:
Read and Reason

News Story

Directions: Choose words from the Word Bank to fill in the blanks for the following news story. Then answer the questions.

Today my mom and dad told me that I will start to receive an allowance on my birthday. Next week, I will be 12 years old! Dad said that I will get my allowance _____, or every second week. Mom said that on my birthday I will have a great "two-wheel" surprise. I bet they are going to give me a _____. Even though I think 12 is pretty old, Mom and Dad told me that our country, the United States of America, is very, very old. They said we had a big _____ celebration when the United States turned 200 years old, but I wasn't even born then!

Word Bank
bicentennial
biceps
bicuspid
bicycle
bifocals
bifold
bilevel
bilingual
biweekly
binary
binoculars
biplane
bisect
biyearly

Questions:

1. Pick out a word that you already know the meaning of. Write the word. What does it mean? _____
   _____

2. Pick out a word you do not know. Write the word. Divide it into parts. What do you think it means? (Remember that *bi-* means "two.") _____
   _____

3. Now look the word up in your dictionary and see whether you figured out the meaning. If you didn't, write the correct meaning here. If you did, use the word in a sentence.

   _____

Part D:
Extend and Explore

Word Sort

Directions: Sometimes *bi-* means "two," but sometimes it doesn't. Which one of these words means "two" and which does not? Put these on the chart in the correct columns.

bilevel	bite	bill	bicycle
biweekly	bitten	biplane	bifocals
bison	bid	bifold	biggest

bi- means "two"	*bi-* doesn't mean "two"

DID YOU KNOW?

In 1976, there was a huge birthday party for the United States of America that lasted for a whole year! It was a "Bicentennial Celebration." Can you figure out how old the United States was? Yes, 200 years old! How old will the United States be for the Tricentennial Celebration in 2076? Here's a hint: *tri-* means "three."

Part E:
Go for the Gold!

Nine Square Wordo

Directions: This game is like Bingo. First, choose a free box and mark it with an X. Then choose eight of the twelve words from the word list provided by your teacher and write one word in each box. You can choose the box for each word. Then, your teacher will give a clue for each word. Make an X in the box for each word you match to the clue. If you get three words in a row, column, or diagonal, call out, "Wordo!"

Part A:
Meet the Root

Divide and Conquer

Directions: "Divide" words into two parts. There is a
Latin number prefix and a base. The bases
have been given to you. Then "conquer"
them by writing the meaning of the words.

	prefix means	base means	word means
1. triangle	three	_angle_ = angle	a shape with three angles
2. tripod		_pod_ = foot	
3. trio		X	
4. tricolor		_color_ = color	
5. trident		_dent_ = tooth, teeth	
6. triple		_ple_ = fold, multiply	
7. triplets		_ple_ = fold, multiply	
8. triplex		_ple_ = fold, multiply	
9. triathlon		_athl_ = contest	
10. trifocals		_foc_ = focus, hearth	

Part B:
Combine and Create

Solving Riddles

Directions: Solve the word riddles. Each answer will begin with *tri-*.

1. I am a two-dimensional figure.
   I have three corners or angles and three sides.
   I also have three syllables. _____

2. I have pedals.
   Young children ride me.
   I have three wheels. _____

3. I happen in baseball.
   I don't happen very often.
   I happen when a team gets three outs on one play.
   I am two words. _____

4. I am a stand for a camera.
   I have three "feet" or "legs."
   I only have two syllables. _____

5. We are three children.
   We were born at the same time.

   _____

6. My name is Neptune.
   I am the Roman god of the sea.
   I use a "three-toothed" fork to catch fish.
   What do you call this three-pronged spear?

   _____

Part C:

Read and Reason

Fill in the Blanks

Word Bank
triangle
triangular
triathlon
tricolor
tricycle
trio
triple
triple-decker
triple play
triplane
triplet
triplicate
tripod
trisect

Directions: Choose words from the Word Bank to fill in the blanks for the following news story. Then answer the questions.

Today in math class we drew a _____, a polygon with three sides. We also looked at a _____ angle that showed how the angles inside the triangle look. Then the math teacher told us we were going to _____ our knowledge of shapes, meaning that we were going to multiply our math skills by three.

Directions: Answer these questions by taking another look at the words in the Word Bank.

1. Pick out a word that you already know the meaning of.
   Write the word. _____

   What does it mean? _____

   _____

2. Pick out a word you are not sure about.
   Write the word. _____
   Divide it into parts. What do you think it means? (Remember that *tri-* means "three.") _____

   _____

3. Pick out a word you do not know at all.
   Write the word. _____
   Divide it into parts. What do you think it means? (Remember that *tri-* means "three.") _____

Part D:
Extend and Explore

Word Sort

Directions: Sometimes *tri-* means "three." Sometimes it doesn't. Put these words on the chart where they belong.

| trinket | trip | triplet | trifocal | trifle | tricycle |
| tribe | tricolor | trim | trick | trio | triple |

tri- means "three"	*tri-* doesn't mean "three"

DID YOU KNOW?

The Roman god of the sea was named Neptune. He had long hair like seaweed and always carried a harpoon, a large pole with *three* prongs. The Romans called this weapon a *trident* because it had three (*tri-*) "teeth." Neptune used his trident to harpoon fish and remind all the sea creatures that he was their king.

Part E:
Go for the Gold!

Nine Square Wordo

Directions: This game is like Bingo. First, choose a free box and mark it with an X. Then choose eight of the twelve words from the word list provided by your teacher and write one word in each box. You can choose the box for each word. Then, your teacher will give a clue for each word. Make an X in the box for each word you match to the clue. If you get three words in a row, column, or diagonal, call out, "Wordo!"

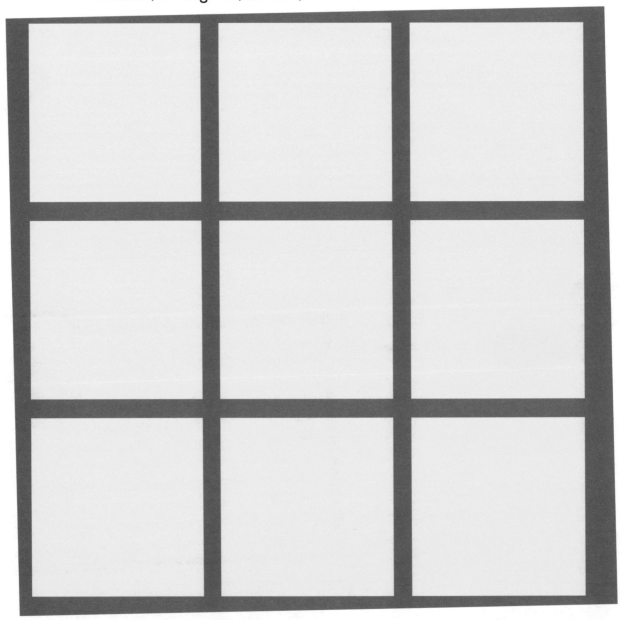

Part A:
Meet the Root

Divide and Conquer

Directions: Your teacher will give you a list of words. "Divide" words into number prefixes and bases. Then "conquer" them by writing the meaning of the words.

	word	prefix means	base means	word means
1.				
2.				
3.				
4.				
5.				
6.				
7.				
8.				
9.				
10.				

Part B:
Combine and Create

Word Scramble

Directions: Unscramble the letters to make words that fit in the blanks.

In the nursery at the hospital, we saw two sets

of _____ .

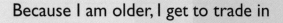

E I L P R S T T

Because I am older, I get to trade in

my _____

for a _____ .

C C E I L R T Y

B C C E I L Y

Nine people are in our singing group, so we call ourselves

a _____   _____ .

E I L P R T

I O R T

Part C:
Read and Reason

Limericks

Directions: *Un-* and *uni-* are two prefixes that can easily be mixed up. *Un-* means "not" when it is at the beginning of a word. This is negative *un-* and is always pronounced with a short *u*. *Uni-* means "one" when it begins a word. The number *uni-* is always pronounced with a long *u*. Read the limerick below. Write the meaning of each *un-* or *uni-* word on the lines provided.

Sometimes unhappy is what I feel

Until I unlock a way to heal.

My friends will unite

When I stop a fight,

And the unity makes friendship real.

unhappy means _____

unlock means _____

unite means _____

unity means _____

Part D:
Extend and Explore

Word Search

Directions: Find the words in the puzzle. Search diagonally, horizontally, vertically, or backwards. Be careful! Some words start the same way!

BIANNUAL	BICYCLE	BIWEEKLY	TRICYCLE
TRIPLE	TRIPLET	UNIFORM	UNISON
	UNIT	UNITED	

D	D	N	J	I	P	N	X	M	Q	I	J	E	O	N
E	A	N	M	D	V	B	R	B	A	N	L	C	R	J
J	E	A	D	R	Z	O	X	L	A	F	P	K	I	F
G	L	X	U	C	F	X	Y	A	H	D	P	D	X	S
K	C	C	X	I	E	A	G	L	T	N	K	L	Z	O
V	Y	W	N	B	V	U	W	X	K	I	C	U	X	Y
I	C	U	B	I	C	Y	C	L	E	E	N	Z	C	F
T	I	E	L	P	I	R	T	J	L	I	E	U	G	I
L	R	H	V	Q	S	Z	D	S	T	W	V	W	E	A
S	T	I	E	T	X	Q	A	E	O	S	U	V	I	X
V	I	X	P	Y	A	X	D	E	Y	Q	N	J	B	B
X	F	Q	K	L	L	A	U	N	N	A	I	B	G	B
T	M	E	D	B	E	E	T	Y	M	R	S	B	O	Y
J	X	I	Y	V	M	T	H	M	C	G	O	K	E	K
M	M	Q	W	P	Y	G	Q	Y	F	U	N	F	V	W

A Final Reflection

Part E:
Go for the Gold!

Directions: Congratulations! You have finished this whole book! Now look back and choose the three roots you liked best. Write them down and tell why they are your favorites!

My Favorite Roots

1. _____

   I like this root because_____

2. _____

   I like this root because_____

3. _____

   I like this root because_____

Now pick out three new words you learned that you think are really interesting. Write the words, and tell why they are your favorites.

Most Interesting Words

1. _____

   I think this is an interesting word because _____

   _____

2. _____

   I think this is an interesting word because _____

   _____

3. _____

   I think this is an interesting word because _____

   _____

Now compare your choices with those of your friends! Did you pick any of the same roots and interesting words?